Shemaz

Eric Orton

Shemaz

Ernst Klett Sprachen
Stuttgart

Eric Orton

Shemaz

1. Auflage   1 [7 6 5 4] | 2014 13 12 11

Internetadresse: www.klett.de / www.lektueren.com

Gestaltung und Satz: Satzkasten, Stuttgart
Umschlaggestaltung: Elmar Feuerbach
Titelbild: Alamy Images Limited / Paul Hakimata
Druck und Bindung: Medienhaus Plump GmbH, Rolandsecker Weg 33, 53619 Rheinbreitbach
Printed in Germany

ISBN 978-3-12-542631-3

Contents

1. A new friend

At one o'clock, the cafeteria of Worcester Sixth Form College was very crowded. Most of the 990 students wanted to get a meal or a quick snack before afternoon lessons started at half past one. So
5 Alan Denby and his friend Mark had to wait a little in front of the food counter.

"Steak pie and double chips, please. Same for you, Alan?" Mark asked.

"No, thanks. I'll have the salad and pizza. Haven't
10 you ever heard of healthy eating, Mark?"

"For heaven's sake! You needn't bore the rest of us with all that rubbish about health food. We all know you want to study medicine. I'm going to sit with Sheila over there. Are you coming?"
15 "No, I'll leave you two alone."

Alan paid for his meal and took his tray. He had to search for a seat in the crowded hall. Then he saw a girl he recognized, a first-year student he occasionally said hello to but did not know
20 personally. She had once asked him for directions – the buildings were very confusing – and he had noticed her ever since. Alan found her attractive with her long dark hair and brown eyes. He sat down opposite her. Alan was eighteen, in his
25 second and last year, and a good student.

"Hello," he said. "Is anyone sitting here?" He had already put down his tray.

"No," the girl said. Alan sat down.

"By the way, I'm Alan. I've seen you around a
30 few times, haven't I? I suppose you know where to

1 **Worcester** [ˈwʊstə] town in England – 1 **Sixth Form College** college for students aged 16-18 (to prepare for A Levels and other exams) – 7 **steak pie** (GB) beef covered with pastry and baked – 18 **to recognize** [ˈrekəgnaɪz] to know who s.o. is because one has seen her/him before – 20 **to ask for directions** to ask the way – 21 **confusing** [kənˈfjuːzɪŋ] here: difficult to find one's way in

find everything now." She smiled and nodded. "I'm Shemaz," she said. He's good-looking, she thought. He's got a friendly smile.

"Are you from India?" Alan asked, trying to make
5 conversation.
"Don't be silly. I'm from Worcester. But my parents came over here from Pakistan in the sixties, if that's what you mean. What subjects do you do, Alan?"
"Oh, I'm doing Maths, Physics and Chemistry. I
10 want to be a doctor. What about you?"
"Maths, Biology and Chemistry. I want to study medicine too." She paused, then said suddenly, "Ah, there's my cousin Rabila. I must go."
"Already?" asked Alan with surprise. "But you
15 haven't finished your meal, and neither have I! Can't you stay a little longer?"
"Sorry, Alan. I shouldn't really be sitting with a stranger. Anyway, I'm doing a computer course at ten past one and I mustn't be late."
20 "Well – er – Can I see you again sometime, Shemaz?" Alan thought quickly. "I've got my car here today. I could take you home at four o'clock."
"Sorry again. My father always comes to fetch me in his taxi. He doesn't like me taking the bus.
25 He didn't want me to come to this college, you see – he's afraid of what might happen to me." She laughed softly. "He only agreed when my mother suggested my cousin Rabila should also study here. She's doing history and music." Shemaz picked up
30 her tray. "I really must go now," she said quickly and started to move off.
"Well, I hope to see you tomorrow."

Alan stared after her. She looked very nice in her Pakistani clothes, but he realized suddenly that he didn't know very much about the Pakistani community or their culture. How frustrating that
5 her father watched her so closely.

Alan mentioned his meeting with Shemaz over supper at home. His mother listened carefully when he told her of Shemaz' situation.

"It's quite surprising because most Pakistani
10 families have been here for a long time, and the parents know that their children have to fit into British society like any other young people here. But some Pakistani parents are still very strict. Usually, those who are Muslims do not drink alcohol. They
15 think that all English boys drink too much alcohol, have low morals and no self-discipline. They fear that if their daughters go out with them, there'll be no chance of a good marriage for the girls later. And when you look at the social problems among
20 white people in some parts of Worcester, you can understand where the fears of these Pakistani parents come from – if that's what they think all young people are like. Aren't there any Indian or Pakistani girls in your class?"
25 "No, there are only two or three in the whole college. But there are quite a few Pakistani boys."

"Well, of course. They have more freedom – some girls from South Asian families have very little. A few Worcester Muslim families even send
30 their daughters back to Pakistan to live with their grandparents. There they are safe from bad influences."

---

4 **community** [kəˈmuːnəti] group of people living together – 5 **closely** *here:* carefully –
13 **strict** *streng* – 14 **Muslim** [ˈmʊslɪm/ˈmʌzlɪm] person who believes in Islam – 16 **low
morals** *lockere Sitten*

"That's awful!" said Alan angrily. "It's so old-fashioned! Poor Shemaz."

Alan's father looked surprised at this. "I hope you're not thinking of going out with her," he said. "Friendships like that bring nothing but trouble. Thirty years ago, we had no Asian people in Worcester at all. And now there are more than two thousand. They run all the taxis and nearly all the sub-post offices. They've bought most of the small corner shops, too, and they're open from seven in the morning until ten at night. I really don't know why the government allowed so many of them to come and work over here."

"Because at that time we needed them to work in our factories and on the railways and buses. We didn't have enough workers," said Mrs Denby patiently to her husband.

"Yes, but now we have three million unemployed. Why are they still here?"

"Come on, Dad! Where exactly can they go? Half of them were born here. This is their home."

"Well, all I'm saying is: don't bring a girl like that home. There must be lots of decent English girls for a boy like you at the college."

"Am I hearing right? 'A girl like that'? What on earth do you mean? You don't even know her. You're prejudiced! None of my friends think like you do, and neither do I. We've been to school with people from lots of different countries or backgrounds. It's no problem for us. They've got just as much right to a job as we have. And why are so many corner shops run by the Pakistanis? I'll tell you why – because the owners and their families work so hard

---

9 **sub-post office** small post office which is part of an ordinary shop – 10 **corner shop** *Tante-Emma-Laden* – 17 **patiently** ['peɪʃntli] in a quiet, slow way – 20 **Come on!** *Na, hör mal!* – 23 **decent** ['diːsnt] nice, acceptable – 27 **prejudiced** ['predʒʊdɪst] disliking s.th. without knowing much about it – 32 **to run** *here:* to manage

and such long hours. Anyway, I haven't brought anyone home yet, have I? And I only talked to the girl for five minutes."

"I'm afraid we'll never agree on this," Alan's father replied. "I think I'll go for a beer."

When his father had gone, Alan asked his mother what she thought about it all.

"I'm not quite sure really. I think you're wrong to say it's not a problem. It's a problem because when people are without a job they often try to find someone to hate. And you mustn't be too naive about the possible difficulties of a friendship like that. But of course you're welcome to bring her here any time. Don't mind your Dad."

The next day, when Alan went to the college cafeteria, he left his friends and started looking for Shemaz. He saw her sitting beside an older Asian girl. "That must be her cousin Rabila," he thought and went to their table. "Hi! Can I get you girls anything?" Alan asked them. Rabila shook her head and got up to leave. "Come on, Shemaz," she said. But Alan could see that Shemaz wanted to stay. "I haven't finished my pudding yet, Rabila. I'll meet you later outside the classroom," she said.

Rabila looked annoyed. She whispered something to Shemaz.

"Oh, it's all right. Alan is doing Chemistry like me. I want him to explain something to me. Go on, I'll see you in ten minutes."

Rabila hesitated, but then turned and walked out.

"Oh dear, she'll tell my father tonight and there'll be an argument," Shemaz told Alan.

5 **to reply** [rɪ'plaɪ] to answer – 14 **to mind** *here:* to pay attention to, to listen to –
25 **annoyed** quite angry – 30 **to hesitate** to pause slightly – 32 **argument** ['ɑːgjʊmənt]
Streit; Diskussion

"This is ridiculous, Shemaz. I've hardly even looked at you!" Alan grinned and went red. "You're not bad though, you know."

"Don't be silly, Alan."

5   "Oh, I'm quite serious. I've already had arguments with my father about you. He was afraid I might want to go out with you. He wants me to go out with a –" – he imitated his father – "– a nice English girl."

10   "That's a good idea. I can't go out with you, Alan."

"What? Not anywhere? Not to a disco or something? Then we'll have to meet in college. When does your last lesson end today, Shemaz?"

"At three."

15   "Right. Will Rabila be free then, too?"

Shemaz paused. "No, she's got a music lesson."

"Great! Then we can go for a walk. I'll meet you here at three."

"Wait a minute! Not so fast! I don't know, Alan. I'd
20   like to, but ..."

"No 'buts'. You're not a child any more!"

"No, in fact I'll be eighteen in September."

"Then for heaven's sake, we can go for a walk, can't we?

25   We needn't make a big drama out of it. See you at three."

Shemaz was very nervous when Alan met her and walked with her out of the back gate. "What will happen if someone sees us, Alan?"

30   "Nothing. Anyway, no one will see us, or, if they do, they won't think it's a crime to go for a walk."

"Don't you mind if your friends see you walking with an Asian girl?"

"For me you are a Worcester girl. And my friends certainly wouldn't mind. Where do you live, by the way?"

"In Merton Lane. You know those little terraced houses? We're Number 43. My father bought it – he works very hard in his taxi business." Shemaz was quiet for a moment, then she said, "He's a very good father, really, even if he is so strict."

Alan took her hand. "I'm sure he is a very good father and just as prejudiced as mine." Shemaz slowly pulled her hand away.

"Have you got any brothers and sisters, Shemaz?"

"I've got two younger sisters and a brother, Aamir. He's sixteen. My sister Sima is twelve, and Sadra is eight. What about you?"

"I've got a sister, Sarah. She's sixteen. You must meet her. She goes to Nunnery Wood School. I think you two would get on well. Then you could come to our house for tea!"

"I've never been to an English house for tea."

"I just can't believe it," said Alan. "Don't you go out at all?"

"Of course I do. At weekends we visit my uncle and his family. They live in North Worcester. And I went to Bradford last summer holiday to see my other uncle. But I never go out during the week, except to the corner shop. It belongs to my mother's cousin."

"That doesn't sound like a lot of fun, Shemaz."

"Well, I'm pretty busy. I haven't got time for fun. My mother isn't very well. She's got asthma and expects me to help with the cleaning and cooking and shopping. I have to look after my younger sisters, too. And then there is all the homework for

---

5 **terraced house** *Reihenhaus* – 18 **to get on well with s.o.** to understand s.o. well, to be friends

the college. By ten o'clock I'm really tired and ready for bed."

"That's no life for a girl of seventeen. I'll have to cheer you up and get you out of the house more often, Shemaz."

"My father would never allow that, Alan. It's really unfair, I think. My brother Aamir can go out when he likes. Just because I'm a girl I have to stay at home all the time. And you know what? My father wants me to marry this year! Nobody ever asks *me* what plans I've made. I want to go to university."

"Marry! Who are you going to marry, Shemaz? You didn't tell me you had a boyfriend!"

"I haven't got a boyfriend, silly. My father is making an arrangement with a cousin of his in Birmingham. He has a son of twenty-five who is a taxi driver like Dad. I haven't met him yet, but he's coming to see us very soon."

"And aren't you worried about marrying a total stranger?"

"Yes, I am. He might be awful, and, anyway, I don't want to get married yet. As I said, I want to study medicine. But my father is against it."

"Isn't there any way you can persuade him, Shemaz? Doesn't he think it would be wonderful for you to be a doctor and do something really useful? Doesn't your father want you to get a good job?"

"No, I think all he wants me to do is marry a good Muslim and clean the house for him and have lots of children. – Oh dear, look at the time, Alan! I must get back. My father is always at the college gate at four o'clock."

"All right, but you must meet me again for coffee tomorrow. I'll introduce you to my sister."

---

15 **arrangement** *here:* plans made by parents for the marriage of a son or daughter –
24 **to persuade** [pə'sweɪd] to make s.o. do sth. by giving good reasons for it

2. Tea at the Denbys'

Shemaz arrived at the college just as the four o'clock bell went. She met her cousin at the gate. "Where have you been, Shemaz? I've been looking for you everywhere. My music teacher was ill, so I went to
5 the library instead. But you weren't there."

"Oh, I went for a walk."

"A walk? Alone? I don't think your father would like that, Shemaz."

"Don't be silly, Rabila. It's not a crime to go for a
10 walk. I had a headache, and the fresh air did me good."

Shemaz' father was already waiting in his taxi outside the gate. "Come on, girls, hurry up. I haven't got time to waste. By the way, Shemaz, Rabila tells
15 me that you were talking to a boy alone yesterday. You haven't seen him again today, have you?"

Rabila wanted to say something, but Shemaz kicked her ankle and she kept quiet.

"You needn't worry, Abba Jhan," Shemaz said
20 to her father in Urdu. "I've had lots of work to do today and no time for gossip."

"As long as you know that you mustn't mix with these students. They have no discipline and no morals. They're a bad influence."

25 Shemaz had heard it all before. She tried not to sound angry. "They're not all the same, Abba Jhan, and I have to mix with them."

"I know you have to be with them in the same class room. But you mustn't sit beside any white boy
30 there or in the cafeteria. Is that quite clear? I only

---

18 **ankle** part of the body between foot and leg – 19 **Abba Jhan** "Dad" in Urdu, the official Pakistani language – 21 **gossip** talk about other people's private lives

want the best for you. Soon you will be married to a good Muslim, and then everything will be all right."

Shemaz did not reply. They drove down the hill to Merton Lane and stopped in front of their small red-brick house. The girls got out quickly, and Mr Asghar drove off to the station. Rabila walked along the road to number 47, where she lived, and Shemaz knocked on the door of number 43. She wasn't allowed to have a key yet. Her youngest sister opened the door and let her into the narrow hall. "I'm afraid Ummi is not feeling very well, Shemaz. She wants you to cook the dinner and then clean the kitchen."

"Well, you can help. I've got a lot of homework to do."

"Sorry, I can't, Shemaz. Sima and I have an invitation to tea from Aunt Kurshid. So you'll have to do it alone. Ummi has also written you a list of things we need from the corner shop. So you'd better start at once."

Shemaz fetched the shopping basket from the larder and walked to the corner shop. This was so full of shelves and freezers that it was difficult to move. There was a strong smell of spices. In front of the shop there were boxes of fruit and vegetables. On the counter inside there were lots of different sweets. Behind it was Nisar Khan, the owner, her mother's cousin. He smiled when he saw Shemaz and said: "Ah, quite the little housewife already. I hear you are getting married. When is the wedding day, Shemaz?"

"Not for a long time, I hope. I want to go to university and study."

5 **brick** *Ziegel- oder Backstein* – 11 **Ummi** *(Urdu)* Mum – 22 **larder** small room for keeping food – 23 **shelves** boards on which things are kept – 24 **spice** *Gewürz* – 30 **wedding** ceremony when you marry

"And what does your father say to that?" "He doesn't like the idea." Shemaz decided not to say any more. "Have you got any samosas left? Ummi is ill in bed and I haven't got time to make any today."

5 "I've got some in the fridge. How many? A dozen?" "Yes, please. And a pound of onions, please."

When Shemaz got back to the house, she made a cup of tea and took it up to her mother. "Are you feeling any better, Ummi? Is there anything else I 10 can get you?" Her mother shook her head.

"Just make sure that the meal is on the table at half past six. You know your father is hungry when he gets home."

Shemaz went back to the kitchen and started to 15 wash the rice when the telephone rang. "618502," said Shemaz.

"It's me – Alan. I'm glad it's you and not your father. Can you talk?"

"What do you think you're doing, Alan? You 20 mustn't ring me at home."

"Aren't you pleased to hear my voice, Shemaz?" Shemaz smiled but said: "You'll get me into trouble, Alan Denby. What do you want now? It's only three hours since we spoke!"

25 "Only? That's a long time, Shemaz! Can't you come out and meet me for an hour or two? We could go to the cafe in New Street."

"Alan, I'm in the middle of cooking dinner. My father will be home in half an hour. Go and do 30 some work and forget about me, right?"

3 **samosa** gefüllte (indische) Teigtasche

"No, it's not all right." There was a pause. "But there's not much I can do, is there? I'll have to wait until tomorrow. See you then, Shemaz. Bye!"

Shemaz sighed. Life was getting more difficult every day. And she hadn't even started her homework. The exam for the end of her first year was on 25th June. She ought to start revising her Biology and Chemistry. She really didn't have time for a boyfriend just now. Shemaz sighed again. She did like Alan.

The next day Shemaz didn't go down to the cafeteria for coffee but stayed in her classroom to do some revision. Ten minutes later, Alan stood beside her table.

"Are you trying to avoid me, Shemaz? Well, you won't shake me off so easily. I've come to tell you that my sister Sarah wants to meet you and will be in our cafeteria at ten past one. Is that all right? Will you be there?"

Shemaz hesitated. "I Don't know, Alan. You're going much too fast for me. And I've got my exams soon. And then there is Rabila ..."

Alan interrupted her: " Please, Shemaz, come and meet my sister. You'll like Sarah. Say you'll come."

"Oh, all right. But now let me go on with my work."

When Shemaz got to the cafeteria, Alan and Sarah were already waiting for her. Sarah was eating sausages, chips and peas. She was a friendly, cheerful blonde. "The sausages here are delicious," she said to Shemaz. "Would you like one?"

---

7 **to revise** [rɪˈvaɪz] *here:* to learn again (for an exam) – 15 **to avoid** to keep away from – 23 **to interrupt** [ɪntəˈrʌpt] to stop s.o. talking by talking oneself – 30 **cheerful** happy, in a good mood

"No, thank you. I eat very little meat, and no pork at all."

"Can I get you something to eat?" Alan asked Shemaz.

5 "A cucumber and tomato sandwich would be nice. Thank you, Alan."

Sarah smiled at Shemaz. "You've certainly made a big impression on my brother, Shemaz. He hasn't stopped talking about you. I'll gladly help you two
10 to meet. Can you come to tea tomorrow?"

"It's very kind of you, Sarah, but I'm really very busy. My mother isn't very well and I've got all this revision to do. Anyway, my father wouldn't like it."

"I have a great idea, Shemaz. I'll come round and
15 ask your father's permission. He won't say 'No' to me, you'll see!"

Sarah hadn't promised too much. She appeared at Shemaz' house that same evening. Mr Asghar had just finished his dinner of chicken tikka masala and
20 was in a good mood.

"I've come to ask you a big favour," Sarah said to him. "I've made friends with your daughter Shemaz, and I'd like to invite her to tea at our house in Beech Road. Could she come tomorrow at five o'clock?"

25 "Shemaz has a lot of housework to do in the afternoon. Her mother is ill in bed."

"I understand, but couldn't her sisters and her cousin do it for her just one afternoon? Please, Mr Asghar. My mother is so looking forward to meeting
30 her."

---

1 **pork** meat from pigs – 5 **cucumber** [ˈkjuːkʌmbə] *Gurke* – 15 **permission** [pəˈmɪʃn] *Erlaubnis* – 19 **chicken tikka masala** pieces of chicken in a spicy sauce – 21 **to ask s.o. a favour** to ask s.o. to do s.th. kind for s.o.

"Beech Road, you say? Well, all right. That's one of the nicer parts of town. But you'll have to come and fetch her. She mustn't travel alone on the bus."

"You needn't worry, Mr Asghar. I'll look after her."

The next afternoon, Sarah came to fetch Shemaz. Alan had parked his car two streets away so that Shemaz' father would not see him. He drove them to a large house with a garden.

Alan's mother came to the door and welcomed Shemaz: "I'm so glad you could come."

They had tea in the living room. There were very thin cucumber sandwiches, buttered scones and a chocolate cake. Shemaz was very shy at first and hardly ate anything, but Mrs Denby was very friendly and asked her a lot of questions about Pakistani food and what kind of books she liked. She lent Shemaz a book on the history of medicine when Shemaz told her about her plans to study.

After tea, Alan showed Shemaz his room. He was very proud of his computer.

"I envy you the peace and quiet of this room," Shemaz told him. "I have to share a bedroom with my two sisters. It is hard to study there, and downstairs the TV is on all the time." Alan nodded. One of his own friends had problems like that.

When they went back to the others, Alan stopped on the stairs and kissed Shemaz. She had never been kissed before and held very still. She touched Alan's cheek with her hand and walked on down.

---

12 **scone** [skɒn] small, plain cake usually eaten with butter – 21 **to envy** *beneiden* –
29 **cheek** [tʃiːk] fleshy part of the face below the eye

3. I don't want my children to mix

In the weeks that followed, Alan and Shemaz saw each other every day, even if sometimes only for a few minutes. Sarah helped them to meet as often as possible. She also persuaded Rabila not to say
5 anything about these meetings. Rabila had always accepted her parents' way of life almost without question. Now her father was arranging a marriage for her, too, and she started to understand how Shemaz felt. She did not like the man who was to
10 be her husband, and she wanted to be a music teacher.

When Shemaz' mother was better, she invited Sarah to tea. Sarah talked a lot, but Mrs Asghar did not know enough English to understand much
15 of her conversation. She just kept filling Sarah's plate with curry and chapattis and afterwards with delicious little cakes. Sarah ate rather too much but had a wonderful time.

At the end of June, Shemaz sat in the big
20 examination hall of the college with its long rows of desks. For four days she answered written questions in Maths, Chemistry and Biology and spent every evening and part of the night revising for the next day. Her hard work was not for nothing.
25 She got A grades in all three subjects, and her tutor, Mr Dukes, told her she should definitely apply for a place at university.

---

16 **chapatti** *indisches Fladenbrot* – 25 **A grade** top mark for schoolwork – 26 **definitely** ['definǝtli] for sure – 26 **to apply for s.th.** to ask for s.th. (e.g. a job) officially in writing

"I'm afraid my father would never allow me to move away and live in a hall of residence, Mr Dukes."

" What if I visited your parents and talked to them about your good work. Would that help? I don't think I've seen them at any of our parents' meetings here at the College, have I?"

"Well, no. My mother hardly goes out at all, and my father didn't really like me coming here. But if you tried to talk to him, it might help. I'd be most grateful, Mr Dukes. I know he thinks education is important for boys, but he thinks girls have an important job in looking after the family and should stay at home. The trouble is, I hate housework, and I don't want to marry yet."

"I quite understand. Let's hope I can persuade your father that we need more Asian women doctors in this country and that you would make a very fine one. You are a very intelligent girl and mustn't waste your chances. Does your father know that you would get financial help while you are at university?"

"Yes, I've told him, but he wants to arrange a marriage with the son of one of his cousins in Birmingham who is a taxi driver. When will you come, Mr Dukes? My father is usually at home between half past six and eight."

"I could come tomorrow. About seven o'clock? Right, see you then."

Shemaz told her parents about Mr Dukes' planned visit. Her mother looked worried and her father angry. He didn't want to argue with a white stranger about his plans for Shemaz. What could

---

2 **hall of residence** *Studentenwohnheim* – 11 **grateful** thankful – 32 **to argue** to discuss the for and against

such a person know about Pakistani traditions? But he received Mr Dukes very politely when he arrived the next evening.

"I want to thank you for all you have done for Shemaz, Mr Dukes. I hear she got high marks in her examination. We are very grateful."

"It's kind of you to say so, Mr Asghar. But it was Shemaz who did all the work. That is the reason I've come this evening. I think Shemaz should apply for a place at university. I and the other teachers think she would probably become a very good doctor."

"That is impossible, Mr Dukes. I hear it takes five or six years to train as a doctor. I've made other plans for her. We've chosen a fine husband for Shemaz. He will marry her very soon. So you can understand, Mr Dukes, that Shemaz won't be coming back to your college in September."

"But don't you think it would be a great honour for her family if Shemaz became a doctor, Mr Asghar?"

"Don't misunderstand me, Mr Dukes. I'm proud of my daughter and want the best for her. But I don't want my children to mix. Our culture is quite different. The students here live in hostels where boys and girls mix, and where some of them drink too much. It's too great a risk. Sorry. Good evening, Mr Dukes, and thank you again."

Shemaz had tears in her eyes when she told Alan about this conversation. They were walking hand-in-hand in the field behind the college. "I just don't know what to do, Alan. My mother doesn't understand, and my father just says I have to marry this man from Birmingham in August."

18 **honour** *Ehre*

"But you say your father loves you."

"You don't understand, Alan. In Pakistani families it's the duty of a daughter to obey her father. And I don't want to hurt his feelings. On the other hand, I'm quite sure that I don't want to marry the man my father has chosen for me. Now that I've met you ..."

Alan kissed her. "Don't worry, Shemaz. We'll find a way out," he said.

A week later, Mabroor Bhatty, the taxi driver from Birmingham, came to Worcester with his parents and was introduced to Shemaz. He didn't say much. He just talked to Shemaz about his taxi. She looked at him and didn't smile. "Why should I marry this stranger? Why do you think he would make me happy?" she asked her father when Mabroor and his parents had left.

"Because he is a good Muslim and because I've known his family for many years. Your mother and I have chosen very carefully. You must trust us. I'm sure you will be very happy. And you'll have a nice little flat in Birmingham. Mabroor works very hard. He is an excellent driver, and he will soon have a second taxi, a newer model."

"Please don't talk to me about taxis, Abba Jhan. I heard all about them this afternoon. The fact is that I don't really like Mabroor. He has nothing interesting to say, and I don't see how I can spend the rest of my life with him."

"I expect you to do your duty as a good daughter, Shemaz. We've already fixed the date of the wedding. It will be on 10th August."

---

3 **to obey** [əˈbeɪ] do what s.o. asks you to do – 23 **excellent** [ˈ---] very good

"Oh no, Abba Jhan, no! I can't! That's in less than a month! Please don't do this to me, Abba Jhan. Don't make me unhappy!"

Her father told her not to worry. "It's all for the best, little flower, you'll see." Then he went out to his taxi to start the evening's work.

Shemaz went up to her room and cried until she fell asleep.

The next morning, she did not wait for her father and left early for college. She waited for Alan in the car park and told him all that had happened. He put an arm around her and said, "You mustn't feel guilty, Shemaz. You're doing nothing wrong. You can't marry someone you don't love."

"But that means I'm not obeying my father, Alan. I really don't know what I can do now; but I'm sure I don't want to marry Mabroor."

"I can't stand the idea of you marrying him either, Shemaz. You must talk to your father again. There's no other way. It can't be wrong for an intelligent girl like you to want to go to university. Give your father the application forms for university and ask him to sign them."

Shemaz did exactly that, but this time her father became really angry. "It's all the fault of that Sixth Form College. The teachers there are putting these silly ideas into your head. I don't want to hear any more arguments now. It's nearly the end of term, so you needn't go back there any more. You are to stay at home from tomorrow and help your mother. Now go to your room. You've made me very angry!" He tore up the application forms and threw them away. Shemaz' mother asked her to think again and

---

13 **guilty** [ˈgɪlti] *schuldig* – 32 **to tear up, tore, torn** to pull to pieces – 32 **application form** piece of paper you have to fill in when you apply for s.th.

to obey her father. But Shemaz was not willing to give up so soon. She went over to her father and said in Urdu:

"I'm sorry, Abba Jhan. I can understand that you are worried about the hall of residence. But I could travel from home to Birmingham University every day – it only takes forty minutes."

Mr Asghar would not listen. "It's just no good, Shemaz. You would still be with all those students all day. You would become like them. Now go to your room. You'll see that in the end you will be quite happy with Mabroor."

The next day Shemaz stayed at home. She was washing the kitchen floor when the telephone rang.

"You go, Shemaz," her mother said. "I don't like answering that thing."

"Hello, hello? Who's speaking?" Shemaz asked.

"It's the Sixth Form College here," said a voice which Shemaz recognized at once. It was Alan's.

"Yes, go on, I'm listening," she said.

"Is that you, Shemaz?"

"Yes, of course."

"Why aren't you at college? Can we meet this afternoon?"

"I'll try."

"Be in the cafe in Friar Street at three o'clock. Nobody will see us there. OK?"

"Yes, thank you for ringing, but I won't be coming to college any more this term. Goodbye." Shemaz hung up and explained to her mother: "That was the college. They wanted to know why I hadn't come this morning."

"Well, I'm glad you told them that you won't go back there." Shemaz was silent. Her mother saw the look of disappointment on her face and added, "Your father really knows best, Shemaz."

5   Shemaz sighed and went on with her cleaning.

At half past two she asked her mother: "Do you want anything from the shops? I'd like to get out of the house for an hour."

"Well, I do need a few things. I'll write you a list."

10   Shemaz was able to reach the cafe by three o'clock. Alan was already waiting. He looked worried. "Are you really not coming back to college, Shemaz?"

"My father has forbidden me to go back, Alan. He 15 just won't listen to me any more. I'm so unhappy." Shemaz started crying. Alan put his arm around her and kissed her.

At that moment the door of the cafe opened. "Taxi for Mrs Pemberton," said a man's voice with a 20 heavy accent. Shemaz looked up in alarm. The taxi driver saw her and rushed over to where they were sitting.

"What do you think you're doing with my daughter?" he cried angrily, bending over Alan. 25 Alan shook.

"So that's why you want to go to university, Shemaz! You want to be together with this boy! I should have known. Well, I've been patient for far too long. Come with me, I'm taking you home. I'm 30 sorry, Mrs Pemberton – this is an emergency. I'll radio for another taxi for you at once."

Shemaz' father took her arm and led her out of the cafe. She turned round to Alan as they went out,

---

14 **to forbid, forbade, forbidden** to tell s.o. not to do s.th. – 20 **alarm** *here:* fear –
24 **to bend over s.o.** *sich über jmd. beugen* – 28 **patient** *tolerant*

and Alan saw the hopelessness in her eyes. He said nothing. He did not want to make things worse for Shemaz, and he was too shocked to speak anyway. People stared as he paid and left.

4. Shut in the house

Back home, Mr Asghar took Shemaz up to her room. "You'll have to stay up here for the next few days. It's quite clear that we can't trust you."

"But, Abba Jhan, please let me explain. I haven't
5 done anything wrong. Alan is just a good friend from college. I ..."
"Don't make excuses. Your mother will bring you some supper later. Now I must go back to work."
Later that afternoon, Alan told his mother about
10 the awful scene in the cafe. "I'm terribly worried about Shemaz, Mum. I don't know what her father will do. He was so angry. I could try and talk to him, but that might make things even worse."
"Perhaps I could come with you. He might listen
15 to me. Perhaps it's all just a big misunderstanding."
"Thanks, Mum! I think we should go at about eight o'clock." Alan was hopeful.
When they arrived at Shemaz' house, Mr Asghar refused to let them come in. "You've done enough
20 damage. Shemaz doesn't want to see you again. Please leave."
Shemaz could hear all this up in her room. She tried to get down the stairs in time, but the front door closed before Alan saw her.
25 Now Shemaz was angry. Why had her father spoken for her that way? Wasn't it *her* life? He was old-fashioned and did not understand. Shemaz felt that colour and cultural differences did not matter to Alan or her. She sat down and wrote

3 **to trust** *(ver)trauen* – 27 **old-fashioned** *opp.* of modern

a letter to Alan. 'Thank you for trying to help. My father will not let me out of the house, but I'll come to see you as soon as I can.' She put the letter in a large envelope and addressed it to Alan. Then she
5 opened the window and looked down. A boy was playing ball in the street. She whistled softly to him and he came over. "I'll give you a pound if you post this letter for me," she said to the boy. "Put a first-class stamp on it, please." He looked surprised but
10 nodded. Shemaz threw the letter and the £1 coin down to him.

Alan received her letter the next morning. He telephoned, but Shemaz' mother put the receiver down when he asked for Shemaz. He went
15 to Shemaz' tutor and told him how her father was keeping her in the house. "Isn't there anything we can do?" he asked.

"Sorry, Alan," the tutor replied. "We have no right to come between a father and his daughter. This is
20 a private family dispute. Let's wait and see. I'm sure Shemaz will be able to see you again in a day or two. Her father can't keep her there for very long."

But after two days, Shemaz was still not allowed to leave the house, and neither her father nor her
25 mother answered her questions. They did not speak to her at all. On the fourth day, her father came to her room and said: "Take this suitcase and pack a few of your things. I'm sending you away from here so you will forget all about that Alan. Your uncle is
30 coming in his car, and we'll take you for a holiday. Please be ready in half an hour."

Shemaz began to cry. "Oh please don't send me away, Abba Jhan!"

6 **softly** *opp.* of loudly – 9 **first-class stamp** in GB there are two classes of post, one quicker than the other – 14 **receiver** part of telephone that you hold to your ear – 20 **dispute** [dɪˈspjuːt] *Streit* – 27 **suitcase** bag for carrying clothes on a trip

"You may stay if you promise to marry Mabroor in August, Shemaz."

"I can't. I really can't, Abba."

"Then you'll have to leave. Perhaps you will see how foolish you are when you are far way from home. Now hurry up and pack!"

Shemaz put a few clothes in the suitcase and wrote a short letter to Alan: "They are sending me away, far away – I don't know where. I'll do all I can to stop it happening or to escape. See you soon. Love, Shemaz." If she dropped this letter in the street, somebody might put it in a letter box.

At half past nine her uncle arrived in his car. Her father carried her suitcase downstairs. "Where are they taking me?" Shemaz whispered to her mother.

"Don't worry, dear. They're taking you to London, to Heathrow Airport. You're going home to Pakistan. There you can stay at my sister's house in Karachi. You'll like it there. It's a beautiful, big city. And you can come back after a year."

"Stay away for a whole year? Ummi, I don't want to go. Please help me!"

"I can't, dear. But you wouldn't be happy with Alan, you know. His family, his home and his religion are all so different. Now do as your father says. He only wants what is best for you." She kissed Shemaz and led her out of the house to the car. The whole family was standing there. At that moment Shemaz made up her mind. She was not going to go to Pakistan for a year. She might never see Alan again, and she would lose her chance of a place at university. Nobody could force her into a marriage

---

5 **foolish** silly and wrong – 29 **to make up one's mind** to decide – 32 **to force s.o. to do s.th.** to make s.o. do s.th.

she didn't want. But she needed a little money to escape, and she knew where she could find some. "Sorry, Abba Jhan," she said. "You'll have to wait for two more minutes. I really must go to the toilet
5 before we leave."

She ran back into the house, rushed to the kitchen and opened the fridge. Her mother kept an old tea tin in there with money for the gas and electricity bills. There were nine ten-pound notes.
10 Shemaz took six of them. Her father was not a poor man and could give them back to her mother. She put the money in an inside pocket, ran to the toilet, flushed it and walked back to the car.

"Write to me as soon as you arrive, dear," said
15 her mother, now in tears. The car drove off, up the London Road and past the Sixth Form College. For a moment, Shemaz thought of jumping out of the car. But no, that was dangerous. She would wait until they reached Heathrow.

20 The trip there took almost three hours. They drove into the short-stay car park. Her uncle took her suitcase. Her father held her tightly by the arm as they walked to the terminal and the ticket counters there. Shemaz had no chance of running off. But
25 while they were waiting in front of the Air Pakistan counter, she said to her father, "I'm afraid I can't wait any longer. I have to go to the ladies' at once."

Her father hesitated. "It's all right," said her uncle. "I'll go with her and wait outside. You stay here and
30 keep her place."

9 **bill** *Rechnung* – 13 **to flush a toilet** to cause water to run through a WC – 22 **tightly** *fest*

Shemaz and her uncle walked to the toilets. When Shemaz was inside, she noticed there was an exit at the other end. She hurried across and found it led almost straight to the exit from the building and the road beyond it. She was free! She started running and did not stop until she got to the tube station. A train had just come in. Shemaz did not understand the ticket machine and asked a young black woman in nurse's uniform for help. The nurse put some coins into the machine, pressed a button and gave Shemaz the ticket. Then they both ran to the platform to the waiting train. Just after they had got in, the doors closed.

"That was lucky! We almost missed it!" said the nurse.

"I'm not very lucky really. I want to go to Newcastle and I don't even know how to get there."

"Newcastle? Is that where you come from?" asked the nurse.

"No. It's where I want to study." Shemaz needed so much to talk to someone that she started telling the woman how she had escaped from her father.

"Why on earth did you run away from your father?" the nurse asked.

"He wanted me to forget my white boyfriend and go to Pakistan for a year."

"Ah, yes. I had endless trouble with white boyfriends. The men in my family hated them. Now I'm married to a Bosnian refugee. My family have accepted him. But some of the neighbours haven't. They don't like seeing a white man with a black woman. I can't repeat some of the things they say

3 **exit** way out – 23 **why on earth ...?** why in heaven's name ...? – 29 **refugee** [ˌrefjʊˈdʒiː] s.o. who had to leave his country because of war, etc.

to us when we go to the pub together. So why do you want to go to Newcastle?"

"Alan, that's my boyfriend, wants to study medicine at the university there like I do. And I think he is planning to go to Newcastle this week to look for a room before term begins. Newcastle is also over two hundred miles north of Worcester, so my parents probably won't look for me there."

"Are you sure you know what you're doing? It's a big step you're taking. What are you going to live on?"

"I know it won't be easy, but I've got £60."

"That won't last very long. And you've got to pay the fare to Newcastle."

"I'll get a job. And I want to finish my A level course but I don't know yet how to do that."

"You could go to evening classes at the Technical College. I did that. But first things first. Telephone your boyfriend and tell him what you are planning to do. Ask him to meet you in Newcastle tonight. When we get to Victoria station – we have to change trains at Earl's Court first – I'll show you the bus station. From there you can get a bus to Newcastle. That's much cheaper than taking the train. Then, when you get to Newcastle, stay in the waiting room until Alan gets there. He'll help you to find a room. It'll be eight or nine o'clock before you get to Newcastle. That's not a good time to walk through a city alone. Do you understand all that?"

"Yes, of course I do. You're very kind. Thank you."

Shemaz and Enid – that was the nurse's name – talked until they reached Victoria. There Enid took Shemaz to the ticket office of the bus station. A

---

14 **fare** price of a ticket for a train, bus, etc.

single ticket cost £17, not as much as Shemaz had feared. They had a cup of tea and a cake before the bus left at half past two. Shemaz also phoned Alan's house. His sister answered the phone: "I'm afraid Alan isn't back yet, Shemaz, but he'll be here by four."

"Oh dear, that'll be too late. Could you do me a great favour and telephone him at the college or go there yourself? It's very important. You see, I've left home and I'm on my way to Newcastle. Please tell Alan I'll wait for him at Newcastle bus station at eight o'clock tonight. But please don't tell anybody else about this. Do you understand?"

Sarah promised to go to the college at once and find Alan.

Enid waited until Shemaz was on the Newcastle bus. She gave her two egg sandwiches and a chocolate bar for the journey and kissed her goodbye. "Good luck, Shemaz. I've written my address and telephone number on this piece of paper. Phone me if you need help." Shemaz waved until the bus was out of the station and on its way through London towards the motorway.

---

1 **single ticket** one-way ticket – 7 **to do s.o. a favour** to do s.th. nice or helpful for s.o.

5. Arrival in Newcastle

The bus got to Newcastle soon after half past seven. Shemaz went to the waiting room. Alan was not there, so she decided to ring her mother. There was a pay telephone in the corner of the room. She put
5 a pound coin in the slot and dialled the Worcester code 01905 and then her parents' number. Her brother answered. Thank heavens it was not her father! "Now listen carefully, Aamir. Don't say anything. Don't tell Abba Jhan who is calling. Just
10 get Ummi and say it's some woman who wants to speak to her. I don't want a long argument with Abba. All right?" After a long pause, Shemaz heard her mother's voice.

"Who is that speaking?"
15 "Don't say anything, Ummi. Just listen. I want to say that I'm safe and you needn't worry about me."
"Not worry?" shouted Shemaz' mother.
"Not so loud, Ummi. My father mustn't know about this call. He'll only get angry again."
20 "He's very worried about you, too. How could you do this to us?"
"I'm also phoning to say sorry about the money I took. I'll pay you back as soon as I've earned enough."
25 "Well, at first I was very angry, Shemaz, very ashamed. But now the money isn't important. Please come back. We are all so worried. Oh, I can hear your father. Are you sure you don't want to speak to him? Then just tell me where you are so I

6 **code** *here: Vorwahl*

can write to you. Your father says he will go to the police and report you as a missing person."

"I'm sorry, Ummi, but I really can't tell you where I am. I won't marry Mabroor and nothing will change my mind. I'll be eighteen quite soon. Then I can do what I like. But I'll always love you, Ummi. I'll think of you every day and I'll telephone again, Ummi. Don't worry. Khooda hafiiz."

"Is that you, Shemaz?" Suddenly her father shouted into the phone. "Have you no respect for your parents? Answer me, Shemaz!"

But Shemaz had put the receiver down. Her father would never understand. She was British and had never been to Pakistan. She sat down to wait for Alan.

An hour passed, and then another. Shemaz walked around the bus station. She was getting very worried. What was she going to do if he couldn't come? She went back to the waiting room.

Ten minutes later, Alan arrived. "I'm so sorry, Shemaz!" he said. He told her he had had a puncture on the motorway.

"I'm just so glad you got here," Shemaz said.

"I was hoping you wouldn't worry too much," he said. "Now let's go and find a room for you first. I can stay in the hall of residence tonight. Later I want to hear everything."

They went out to Alan's car, and in Jesmond Road they found a bed and breakfast for Shemaz. Later, in the cafe opposite, Shemaz told Alan all that had happened that day.

"I think you're great," said Alan. "I don't know if I would have had the courage to do what you did."

---

4 **to change s.o.'s mind** to make s.o. have a different opinion – 8 **khooda hafiiz** (*Urdu*) goodbye – 22 **puncture** small hole in a tyre – 22 **motorway** *(GB) Autobahn* – 29 **bed and breakfast** *Frühstückspension*

"Well, thanks, but it's not over yet. We have to plan. Where can I start looking for work? And somewhere to stay?"

Alan thought for a minute. "Tomorrow we could
5 go to the Citizen's Advice Bureau."

<hr />

5 **Citizen's Advice Bureau** *(GB)* office where you can go for advice about, e.g., money or housing problems

6. A fresh start

Staying at the bed and breakfast was a new experience for Shemaz. She was not used to having a room alone. It took a while for her to get to sleep. Many thoughts were going through her mind.

Next morning Alan picked Shemaz up and took her to the Citizen's Advice Bureau. There they had to wait for over an hour. There were so many people there with problems. At last it was Shemaz' turn. She got up and went into the interview room.

A lady with white hair was sitting behind a desk. "Sit down and tell me how we can help, dear."

Shemaz explained why she had left home. "I spent last night at a bed and breakfast place in Jesmond Road," she said, "But it is too expensive for me. I've only got £34 left. So I'd like to find a room as soon as possible – with a family, if I can. My father would not find me as easily in a private house. You see, I won't be eighteen until September."

The woman thought for a minute. "I should really tell you to go back home – but I can see that wouldn't help you. And you'll be eighteen soon anyway." She paused. "So you'll need a room as well as a job. Your £34 won't last very long. Have you any idea what sort of job you want?"

"I have to try and finish my A levels here – my father made me leave the Sixth Form College. Perhaps I could go to evening classes at the Technical College and work as a waitress during the day."

"Yes, that might be possible. I know the manageress of the cafeteria in the university union. She may have a job for you. I'll phone her now."

She dialled and said: "Hello! Hazel?" This is Mary
5 Watson. I've got a young girl here with me. She's seventeen. She wants to go to evening classes to get her A levels and work during the day, so she needs money for a room. She seems a very sensible girl. Do you think you could help her? Yes? Oh, that's
10 wonderful. What are the hours? And the pay? Right, thank you, Hazel. I'll send her to you this afternoon. Her name is Shemaz Asghar. What? A-s-g-h-a-r. That's right. Thank you. Bye."

Shemaz watched while the woman quickly made
15 some notes. Then she looked up. "Well, Shemaz. This is your lucky day. It's not always easy to find a job; but the manageress can use you in the cafeteria. You'll have to clean the tables and work behind the counter."

20 "What else will I have to do there?"

"Oh, serve the food, sell tea and coffee, heat meals in the microwave and take the money. They have an electronic cash register there. Do you think you could learn to use it?"

25 "No problem."

"Fine! Now to your second problem – a room. That may not be so easy. Rooms can cost £60 a week or more, and you can't really afford that much. Oh, I forgot to tell you – they'll pay you £2.90 an hour,
30 and you'll have to work from 9.30 a.m. to 5.30 p.m. Mondays to Fridays – that's a 40-hour week. So you'll get £116 gross and about £90 net."

---

2 **university union** clubhouse for students – 10 **pay** *here:* what you are paid for a job –
22 **microwave** ['maɪkrəʊ'weɪv] small electric oven for cooking things very quickly –
23 **cash register** machine for adding and recording money paid – 32 **gross** *brutto*

"What's 'net'?" Shemaz asked.

"What is left of your pay after national insurance and tax. Now about your room. Perhaps an Asian family would help. I don't know any Asians in Newcastle myself, but my daughter works in the university hospital and ..."

"An Asian family may not like the fact that I have a white boyfriend and have run away from home," Shemaz interrupted.

"True, but a white family may not like it either. Don't forget that a lot of white young people have conflicts with their parents, too. We'll have to be very careful and find somebody sensible and liberal. Let me talk to my daughter tonight, Shemaz. Come back tomorrow at ten o'clock. All right?"

"Yes, thank you. I'm very grateful."

"OK. Go and see the manageress this afternoon. Her name is Hazel Carter. I think you'll find it quite easy to work for her. She's a very fair woman."

When Shemaz told Alan about her interview, he was very pleased. "That's great news, Shemaz. We're making real progress. Now I'll show you the university, and then we can have a meal at the cafeteria in the union."

When they got to the cafeteria at half past one, there was still a long queue from the door to the food counter. "I can see why they need extra help here," said Alan. "Probably the cafeteria is popular because the prices are low. Look at the menu on that board – jacket potato, sausages and baked beans cost only 90p and bread-and-butter pudding 65p. That's why they're paying you so little. It's disgusting!"

---

2 **national insurance** *(GB) Sozialversicherung* – 26 **queue** [kjuː] line of people waiting –
30 **jacket potato** large baked potato eaten with the skin

"Don't say that, Alan. I'm very lucky to get a job so quickly. I'll go and find two seats. I don't want to talk to the manageress when she is so busy."

"OK. What would you like, Shemaz?"

5 "A cheese salad and orange juice, please."

An hour later, when there was no queue, Shemaz introduced herself to Hazel Carter. She took her into her office and said: "I must be quite honest with you, pet. This is not an easy job. The students 10 don't like waiting and can be quite rude. So you'll have to be quick and not mind their silly jokes. And you'll have to do all kinds of jobs, even wash the floor in the morning. Would you mind doing that?"

"No, of course not. I cleaned a lot at home."

15 "Can you remember prices and use an electronic cash register?"

"I think I can learn quickly, Mrs Carter."

"Fine! So when can you start? I need help as soon as possible. I caught one of the girls stealing and 20 she had to go."

"I can start the day after tomorrow, Mrs Carter. Tomorrow I'm seeing Mrs Watson at the Citizens' Advice Bureau about a room; but after that I'm free. What shall I wear to work? I haven't got many 25 clothes here."

"Don't worry. We provide overalls for all our assistants. Right, I'll expect you the day after tomorrow then."

Mary Watson had good news for Shemaz the 30 next morning. "My daughter knows a Pakistani nurse – Jemella Panting. She's married to a white engineer. They have a large house in Eskdale Terrace and can let you have a room with breakfast

8 **honest** not lying or stealing – 9 **pet** *here:* dear – 26 **overall** ['əʊvərɔːl] clothes you wear over other clothes at work

and evening meal for £60 a week. That won't leave you with a lot of pocket money, but it's really quite cheap and you'll have a friendly home with people who understand your problem. My daughter has already spoken to Mrs Panting. She is looking forward to meeting you this evening. Any time after seven o'clock. It's 29 Eskdale Terrace and the phone number is 684314."

"Thank you very much, Mrs Watson. Now my only worry is my father. He's probably gone to the police and asked them to find me and bring me back to Worcester."

"The police might not have the time to do that, Shemaz. They would definitely try and find a child of seven, but not a girl of seventeen. Dozens of teenagers run away from home every week, and their parents come here and ask us to search for them. Sadly we can't help them. But you must be careful. Tell Jemella Panting your father is looking for you. She mustn't tell your story to other Asians here in Newcastle. It's quite possible your father will write to mosques in different parts of the country and ask for help in finding you."

"Oh dear," said Shemaz, "I hate hiding like this. I don't want to hurt my parents; but my studies and my boyfriend are important to me, and I have to go my own way."

"Well, let's hope you can persuade your father. Remember, as soon as you are eighteen, you can plan your own life and won't have to ask your father. Perhaps you'll even get on with him better then. Come back and see me if you need more advice. Goodbye, Shemaz, and good luck!"

---

15 **dozens** *here:* lots of, very many – 22 **mosque** [mɒsk] building where Muslims say their prayers – 25 **studies** period of learning

Shemaz met Alan for lunch and told him about her room and what Mrs Watson had said: "I'm really worried, Alan. If my father finds me here and makes me go back to Worcester or to Pakistan –
5 well, I don't know what I'd do!"

"He won't find you if you're careful, Shemaz. And you'll be eighteen soon. When I go back to Worcester tomorrow ..."

"Tomorrow? Oh, Alan! I'll feel lonely here without
10 you."

"I'll be back after the weekend, I promise. You see, I've got to get the rest of my things. And I'll have a chance to talk to my mother. Perhaps she and I could go and see your mother and tell her you're all
15 right."

"I'd like that, Alan. Thank you. But go when my father is out in his taxi and when my sister Sima is at home. She can interpret. My mother's English isn't very good."

20 "I'll go in the afternoon. This evening I'll take you to Eskdale Terrace. Then you can see if it is all right, and I can see where you'll be living."

---

18 **to interpret** [ɪnˈtɜːprɪt] to translate spoken language immediately into another one

7. A place to live

At seven that evening, Shemaz rang the bell at 29 Eskdale Terrace. A woman in nurse's uniform opened the door. "Hello, Shemaz. I'm Jemella," she said.

5 "Pleased to meet you," said Shemaz. She was nervous. "This is my friend Alan Denby."

"Hello, Alan. Come in and meet my husband. I've told him all about you."

They went into the living room. There Jemella
10 introduced them to her husband Barry. Shemaz quickly explained her situation.

"Jemella had the same problem," Barry said to Shemaz.

Jemella nodded. "I know how difficult it is to
15 leave home against the wishes of your parents. And it wasn't easy for Barry either. But we both get on with my parents now. We're going to visit them later this year."

"It's my father who's been the problem," said
20 Barry. "He doesn't like telling his friends at the pub that his son is married to a Pakistani. What about your parents, Alan? What do they think?"

"My mother likes Shemaz very much, but my father is prejudiced, too, I'm afraid. I hope he
25 will change his mind when he really gets to know Shemaz."

"Are you staying near here, Alan?" Jemella asked.

"Yes, I've got a room in a hall of residence. So that's not a problem."

"No," said Shemaz, "The problem is that my father has probably gone to the police and asked them and his friends in the Asian community to look for me. So I'd be most grateful if you wouldn't
5 talk about me to your friends and neighbours. The fewer people who know my story the better."

"Your secret is safe with us, Shemaz," said Jemella. "Now come and have a look at your room. Afterwards we can have some coffee before I go
10 back to the hospital. I'm working tonight."

Shemaz liked the room very much. There were new curtains, bookshelves full of paperbacks and a comfortable chair beside the bed. And it felt a bit like home being with another Asian woman.

15 Alan left soon after. He had to go home early the next morning, and Shemaz had to start work at the cafeteria.

The next day, Hazel Carter was very glad to see Shemaz when she arrived at half past nine. "The
20 first big crowd of students comes in at half past ten for coffee and snacks. So we have just an hour to clean the tables and do the vegetables for lunch. It's Lancashire Hotpot today, so you'll have to cut up lots of carrots. OK?"

25 "No problem," Shemaz replied. The first hour went by very quickly, and before she knew it she was standing behind the counter, selling cups of coffee and chocolate biscuits. By the end of the day she was very tired.

30 The next day, at a time when things were not very busy, an Asian girl student spoke to Shemaz while

---

9 **afterwards** [ˈɑːftəwədz] after that – 12 **curtains** [ˈkɜːtnz] cloth hanging at both sides of a window – 12 **paperback** *Taschenbuch* – 23 **hotpot** dish of meat, potatoes and vegetables

she was serving her. "You're new here, aren't you?" she said. "Do you perhaps come from Worcester?"

"No," Shemaz lied. "Why do you ask?"

5 "Oh, there's a notice in a Pakistani grocery shop near here. It asks for information about a Shemaz Asghar who has run away from her home in Worcester."

Shemaz was shocked but tried not to show it. The girl seemed to understand. "Don't worry if you are 10 Shemaz. I won't tell anyone. Listen, shall we have a cup of coffee together when you have a moment?"

Shemaz was able to take a break soon after, so they sat down together. Shemaz trusted the girl, who told Shemaz her name was Armina Bibi, and 15 they talked about their situations. "I know how difficult things can get at home," Armina said. "Our parents weren't born here and didn't go to school here. They come from a different world, don't they, in which women mostly have to stay at home and 20 obey the men in everything. I sometimes feel like a prisoner at home. Luckily my father had a very good education and wants one for me too. So he has allowed me to go to university. But be careful here," she warned Shemaz. "Don't tell people your 25 name unless you have to."

"Thanks for the advice," said Shemaz. She was not happy about the notice in the Pakistani shop. On the other hand, it was good to find a new friend.

Shemaz was glad when her eight hours at the 30 cafeteria were over and she could go home to Eskdale Terrace. Jemella was cooking a big meal of lamb curry with rice and nan bread. As Ramadan

---

4 **grocery shop** *Lebensmittelladen* – 32 **lamb** [læm] meat of young sheep –
32 **nan bread** *indisches Fladenbrot* – 32 **Ramadan** period of fasting for Muslims

started the next day, they were then forbidden to eat during the hours of daylight for thirty days.

Alan phoned later that evening and told her the latest news: "Mum and I went to see your mother this afternoon. She didn't want to let us in at first, but Mum persuaded her. Your mother was very pleased to hear you're all right and staying with a Pakistani nurse. She wanted to know your address, of course. Mum explained that I had promised you not to tell anyone, which your mother naturally didn't like. But there's nothing we can do about that. She didn't want us to stay for long because she thought your father would get back from the mosque very soon. He's still very angry that you ran away. When we left, we promised to go there again with more news about you. Your mother gave me some clothes for you, by the way. And your sister was a very good interpreter."

Shemaz felt better. "That's good, Alan. Thank you for all your help. Are you coming back to Newcastle soon? I miss you!"

"I'm thinking of you all the time, Shemaz. I'll be back Monday afternoon. See you then!"

Shemaz was happier now and enjoyed her job the next day. Hazel, the manageress, was pleased with her good work and invited her to a meal of spring rolls and salad. She was surprised when Shemaz refused: "I've started my Ramadan fast today. Muslims are not allowed to eat anything during the day."

"But you must eat something when you are working all day. A little snack doesn't count, does it?"

28 **fast** period when you are not allowed to eat

"I'm afraid it does. I still feel strongly about those traditions, even though I sometimes feel a little mixed up. At my Sixth Form College I often felt more Pakistani than at home; and at home I sometimes
5 felt very English compared to my family."

"It sounds like your parents follow their religion very closely."

"Yes, they do. As a good Muslim, my father prays five times a day. He doesn't like the English way of
10 life and usually speaks to me in Urdu. He always felt that the students at my college had no standards and no discipline and little religion. I know what he meant and that he only wanted the best for me. But he couldn't understand that I wanted to mix with
15 everyone at college and wanted more freedom and the best of both cultures."

"That's only natural if you grew up here. So don't feel guilty. How long is your fast?"

"A month. But I can have a big meal every evening
20 after sundown. So I'll be all right, thanks."

The next morning, after a very early breakfast, Shemaz went to the Technical College and booked evening classes in Biology, Chemistry and Maths. Hazel let her do that before she started work. And
25 on Saturday, Jemella and Barry invited her to come with them to a party at a friend's house. Shemaz had a wonderful time and danced until midnight. She had never been to a party like that before.

Shemaz felt like a new world was opening up for
30 her.

Alan returned on the Monday as he had promised, and his mother came with him. She invited Shemaz and Jemella for a late meal at her hotel. Over coffee

---

8 **to pray** to speak to God to give thanks or to ask for s.th.

and chocolates, Mrs Denby told Shemaz why she had come with Alan. "I wanted to see his room and help him to make it comfortable. But I also wanted to talk to you about your mother. Don't you think you could now telephone her and tell her where you are? I know she is still very worried about you."

"Yes, I know and I feel awful about that. But my father still wants an arranged marriage for me. He won't give up."

"Yes, but what about your mother? Can't you at least telephone her?"

"I really don't know what to do. I don't want to hurt her, but I've made up my mind."

"What's your advice, Jemella?" Mrs Denby asked.

"We can't ask Shemaz' mother not to tell her husband. And I can understand Shemaz' father. He wants to protect her and do what he thinks is right. My own father was the same. He was furious when I started going out with Barry. For two long years he refused to meet him. So I left home and went to live in the nurse's hostel here. But I never gave up. He's a very proud man and came to England from a very small village in Pakistan. It wasn't easy for him to understand the English way of life. I think it'll be best if Shemaz waits until she is eighteen. Then she is free to stay in Newcastle and to study – even if her parents still say no. But after that she must try and explain to her parents what she is trying to do."

Mrs Denby listened to Jemella. After all, Jemella knew what she was talking about. So Mrs Denby did not say any more about Shemaz' mother. She took Shemaz up to her room. There she gave her the clothes she had brought from Worcester for her.

"Your sister Sima sends her love. She also gave me your college notes and books for you. She thought they could be useful."

"Thank you, Mrs Denby, they certainly will be a
5 great help."

"And I also have a lovely surprise for you, Shemaz. It's from your friends in the Sixth Form College."

Shemaz opened the brightly wrapped parcel. In it was a long silk scarf in different shades of orange
10 and red. There was a card with it that said:

'*Dear Shemaz,*

You are not forgotten. We wish you lots of luck in your new life.

Very best wishes from the 6b tutor group.'

15 Shemaz was over the moon. She put on the scarf at once. "You look great!" Alan said when she came downstairs wearing it.

When Mrs Denby returned to Worcester two days later, Alan started looking for a holiday job. He got
20 one as assistant porter at the hospital. "Just until term starts in October," he explained to Shemaz. At the end of his first day, he met her at the union cafeteria. "How are you this evening?" he asked her.

"It's not easy serving food for eight hours when
25 you're fasting, Alan. I'm so hungry I could eat a horse. Never mind. I mustn't think about it. That's the only way. What sort of day have you had?"

"I feel tired! But it's been very interesting. I'm working in the Casualty Department. You see
30 some awful things there. But I had the chance to talk to a lot of patients. There was one Pakistani woman there, but she didn't understand a word of what I was saying. A doctor told me that like a

---

15 **over the moon** *(informal)* very happy – 20 **assistant porter** *here:* s.o. who takes patients to different parts of a hospital – 29 **casualty** [ˈkæʒjuəlti] **department** place in hospital for people hurt in accidents

lot of other Asian women she only went out to the Pakistani corner shop and didn't know any English at all. 'We'll have to get an interpreter to find out how long she has had this pain,' he told me. I can't believe these women are so cut off!"

"Some of them still are," Shemaz replied. "Look at my mother, for example. I wonder if there are any English classes for these women. The men go out to work and learn English there; but a lot of the women stay at home all the time and don't even know enough English to ask a neighbour for some milk. I'd really like to help Pakistani women like my mother learn English ..."

"It's a good idea, Shemaz; but you won't have a lot of time to give English lessons."

"No. But I must ask Jemella whether there are lessons the women can go to. Perhaps we could find other students who are interested in teaching them – and I could talk to the women so that they have the courage to go to the lessons. Would you teach, too?"

"Of course I would – if I were good enough."

5 **cut off** isolated

8. In the headlines

Jemella smiled when she heard Shemaz' idea. "An Asian social worker tried to start classes last year. But it's very difficult to find people to teach the women. It is all voluntary. The social worker gave up the idea because she was so busy. So it would be good if you could find someone to help. But you two have got enough to do!" She then said slowly, "Perhaps I could help out, too. But Shemaz, wait till after your birthday!"

Shemaz could hardly wait to turn eighteen. She counted the days till her birthday. Together with Jemella and Barry, she and Alan organized a party at Eskdale Terrace.

A few college friends came, too, and stayed overnight in sleeping bags on the living room floor. At the party there were three different curries, Tandoori chicken, delicious pear tarts and an upside-down pineapple pudding. It was, after all, the day Shemaz was really free to decide her own future. She phoned her family that day and spoke to her mother and sisters. Her brother was out, and her father did not want to come to the phone. This time she gave her mother her address and promised to visit them as soon as possible.

At the hospital, Alan put up a notice about the English lessons. A week later, Shemaz, Alan, Jemella and the social worker met eight other people at the hospital who were interested in helping. They were all from different ethnic backgrounds and included

---

4 **voluntary** *freiwillig* – 17 **pear** *Birne* – 18 **pineapple** *Ananas*

medical students, nurses and a doctor. Armina came along, too.

"The hospital managers have offered us a room which we can use for our lessons," Shemaz
5 explained after they had introduced themselves. "The question is: When is the best time to teach these women?"

"Well, we're probably not all free at the same time every week," said Jemella. "So let's have two
10 small classes, one in the evening from eight until nine and one in the afternoon at two o'clock. The children are at school then and the husbands are at work. The problem is, how do we let the women know about these English lessons?"

15 "Can I make a suggestion?" the doctor asked. "Put up notices in sub-post offices. Asians manage most of them, and many of the women go there once a week to get their child benefit."

"A good idea," said Shemaz. "We could also send
20 the notice to the local paper, *The Newcastle Journal*. That could be in English, and the one for the sub-post offices in Urdu and Punjabi. Any suggestions for the English text of the notice?"

"What about something like this?" said a male
25 nurse.

'*To all Asian women in Newcastle:*
Would you like to learn English?
Students, doctors and nurses from your hospital offer free lessons. Come to the Royal Free Hospital in
30 *the centre of Newcastle on Tuesdays from 2-3 p.m. or on Thursdays from 8-9 p.m. Learn how to talk to your doctor and your bank clerk, and how to fill in*

---

18 **child benefit** money given to parents by the state for a child – 22 **Punjabi** [pʌnˈdʒɑːbiː] language of people in the Punjab in northwestern India and Pakistan – 24 **male nurse** *Pfleger* – 32 **bank clerk** [klɑːk] s.o. who works in a bank

forms. Meet other Asian women. All are welcome. For more information phone Shemaz Asghar.'

"This is great!" said another nurse. "When can we start?"

5 "Not yet," said Alan. "First we have to learn what to teach. I have spoken to a professor in the English department of the university here. He has agreed to come and talk to us about methods. He will also bring us some books, and he suggested we ask local 10 businesses to support us by paying for books. So I don't think we can start for a while yet."

"We must all try and make the lessons as easy as possible," Shemaz added. "Some of the women have come from small Pakistani villages and left 15 school when they were ten. So they don't know any English at all. We have to teach them the names of the days and months, numbers and parts of the body, the colours and the names of vegetables."

"What about the women who can't leave the 20 house because they have very small children?" a canteen assistant asked.

"A good point," said Jemella. "As we now have ten teachers here, two or three of us could go and visit those women in their own homes."

25 "We could also make up some easy dialogues and record them on cassettes," suggested Shemaz.

"I've got a camcorder," said a student. "We could video a conversation about buying stamps and an aerogramme at the post office, or about a visit to 30 the housing department."

They went on with their discussion for another half an hour and then agreed to meet again the next

10 **to support** *unterstützen* – 30 **housing department** *Wohnungsamt*

Thursday evening to listen to the English professor. Three weeks later, Jemella and Armina started the first evening class with seven women, and Alan and the other nurse the afternoon class with eight
5 women. Shemaz did not have the time to teach but helped with the organization. Some of the women were very shy and just laughed when Alan said: "Repeat after me: January ... "

Three weeks after that, a reporter from the
10 *Newcastle Journal* came to the hospital and wanted to interview Shemaz about her English lessons for Asian women. At first she refused. "My friend Alan can answer your questions much better. I don't want to be in the paper."
15 "But this project was your idea, wasn't it? Right, so I want to interview you. You probably understand the problems of Asian women in our city much better. Tell us, why did you think English classes for Asian women so important? And why did you
20 choose nurses and students to be the teachers?"
"Well, nurses see the problem every day, and there are a lot of students who are angry about racism, about the posters saying "Pakis go home!". So they are keen to help Asian women. They want
25 to make it easier for them to understand their white neighbours and to learn that white people in Newcastle are not all prejudiced."
"And you? What do you want, Shemaz?"
"I want to build bridges between our cultures. I'm
30 English, born in Worcester; but I'm also a Muslim of Pakistani origin."

---

23 **Paki** impolite word for a Pakistani – 24 **keen** very interested in doing s.th. – 31 **origin** ['ɒrɪdʒɪn] where s.o./s.th. comes from

The paper printed quite a long report on the project. There was a photo of Shemaz with one of the women learning English. Both were smiling. Shemaz sent the article and the photo to her parents.

Mrs Asghar asked her husband to translate.

"Do you see?" she said to him. "She hasn't given up her Pakistani traditions at all." She was proud of her daughter. Her husband said nothing at first, but he stared at the photo for a long time.

"Will you forgive her?" asked his wife.

"Not yet," he said.

"A Pakistani woman doctor would understand the problems of Pakistani women very well," she said. "And don't you want to see her at home in the holidays?" He did not reply. Mrs Asghar decided not to say any more.

A week later Shemaz came home to visit. There was a big welcome from everyone except her father, who just nodded his head. Her mother had prepared a huge meal of lamb curry and lots of sweet cakes. Afterwards, Shemaz and her parents had a long talk. First, her father said again how angry he was that she had run away. Shemaz listened but saw that he was not really as angry as he had been. She told her parents all about her job, her room in Jemella's house and her plans for studying medicine. "Will you sign my application forms for university now, Abba Jhan?" she asked.

Her father looked down at the floor. "You have refused an arranged marriage, Shemaz. My friends will say one cannot trust you. It will be difficult to find another man for you."

"Good. I don't want another man. I'm only eighteen. I want to study first. And I promise to be
5 a good Muslim daughter and a useful member of the British community." She looked straight at her father as she said this.

"And will you promise not to marry Alan at once but wait?"

10 "I promise. Can we forget about Mabroor?"

"I feel ashamed, Shemaz. I have broken a promise."

"But what's more important – your promise or my happiness? I was born in this country! Will
15 you speak to Mabroor and his father? Please, Abba Jhan!"

Mr Asghar paused for a long time. Shemaz was very nervous.

"All right," he said at last, taking a deep breath. "I
20 will pray to Allah that your life in Newcastle will be that of a good Muslim. But I don't like your job in the cafeteria. I'll give you money so you can study during the day. Now give me the application forms. I suppose a doctor in the family could be quite
25 useful. There's this pain I sometimes get in my left leg ..."

Questions and activities

Pre-reading:

Which ethnic groups do you know of in Britain? How is the situation different from your own country?

Chapter 1

1. When did most Pakistanis come to England and what kinds of jobs were they needed for at first?
2. What differences do there seem to be between white British families and families of Pakistani origin?

Chapter 2

1. Explain why Shemaz' father is so against her mixing with white students.
2. Do you think it is a good idea (or even possible) for different ethnic groups to live completely separately within a multicultural society? Give reasons for your answer.

Chapter 3

1. Why did Shemaz' parents not go to parents' meetings at the school?
2. Do you know of cases in your own country, where a *girl* was not allowed to go on to higher education? What reasons were given?
3. In several countries there is still a tradition of arranged marriages. Think of arguments *for* and *against* such arrangements.

Chapter 4

1. Write Shemaz' diary from the time her father takes her up to her room till her uncle arrives to drive her to London.
2. The reaction of Shemaz' father to the situation seems very extreme. Do you know of other cases of conflict between the generations where the reaction of the parents was rather drastic? Describe them.
3. What advice would *you* have given Shemaz if you had met her on the tube at Heathrow?

Chapter 5

1. Would you have phoned your mother if you were in Shemaz' position? Say why or why not.
2. What would your parents do if you ran away?

Chapter 6

1. Write Shemaz' diary for her first day in Newcastle.
2. Does Shemaz' new job seem badly paid in your opinion? Should she have refused it? Give reasons.

Chapter 7

1. Explain why Jemella can understand Shemaz' problems so well.
2. Write a short report on *Ramadan.* Check the facts in an encyclopedia or other books of reference. Compare it with Catholic Lent *(Fastenzeit).*
3. How does Shemaz want to help Asian women?

Chapter 8

1. How does Shemaz' plan develop?
2. Write the newspaper article about Shemaz' project for the *Newcastle Journal.*

Post-reading:

1. What bridges could be built between different cultures in your own society?
2. *Project:* Choose one minority group in your own country. Find out where they came from and why, as well as what problems they have in their new home.